Revised
Practice in Music Theory

Josephine Koh

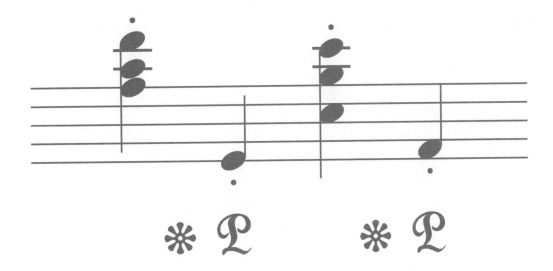

Grade 2

Based on the music theory syllabus of the Associated Board of the Royal Schools of Music

Copyright © 2010, 2008 by Wells Music Publishers
ISBN 981-05-6166-6

Wells Music Publishers
29A Binjai Park
Singapore 589831

First edition published in 1991 © by Music Plaza Pte Ltd
Second edition published in 2005 © by Yamaha Music (Asia) Pte Ltd

Cover design : Lee Kowling
Typesetting : Ching Zong Yi, Leon Foo, Poon Ken Min
Editorial : David Saw

INTERNATIONAL SALES ENQUIRES:

Wells Music Publishers,
29A Binjai Park
Singapore 589831
Tel: +65-64682928
Fax: +65-64687162
Email: info.wmp@gmail.com
Website: www.wellsmusicpublishers.com

Contents

Ledger Lines

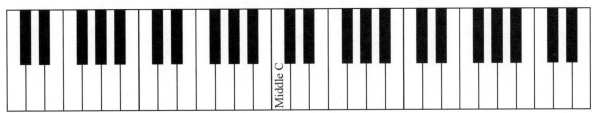

Notice from the above diagram that **ledger lines** are used for notes that lie above or below the stave. *(At grade 2, up to 2 ledger lines are used).*

> 1. Copy and name these notes. Make sure that the ledger lines are straight and are at the same distance away from the stave lines.

a)

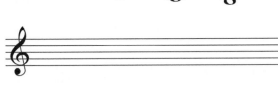

b)

c)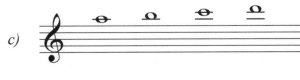

d)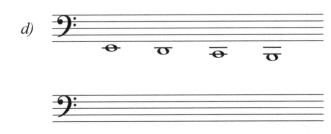

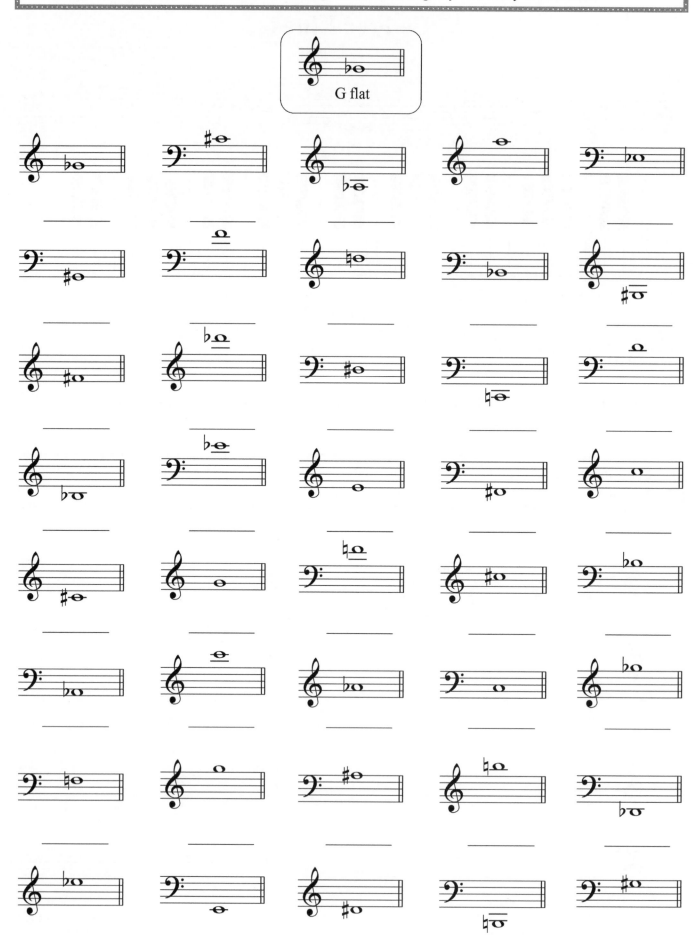

G flat

3. Write the notes of the same pitch in the other clef in each of the following. You may use the keyboard on page 1 to help you.

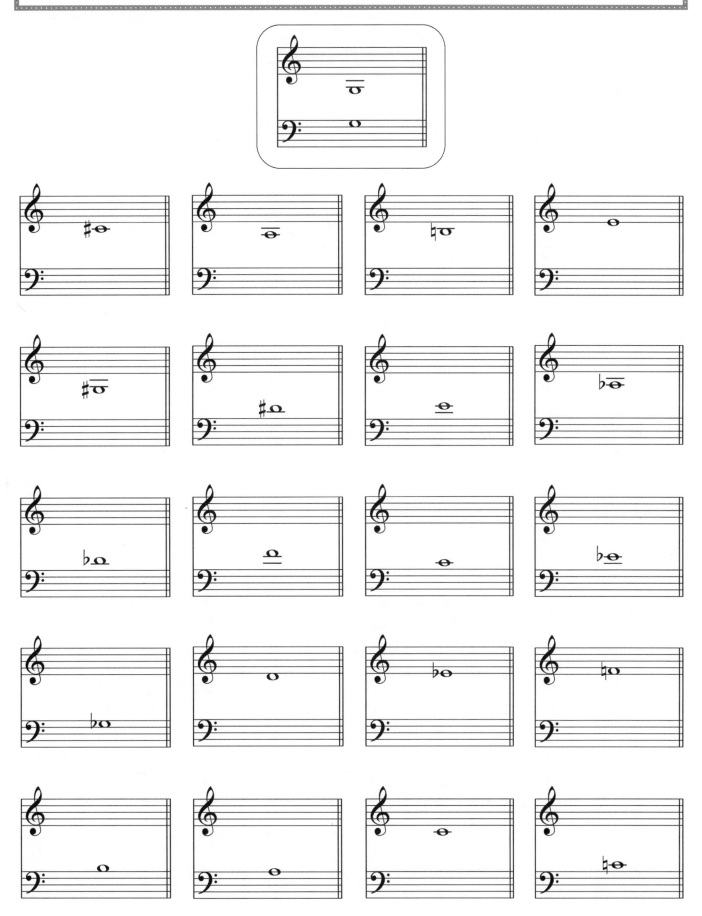

4. Rewrite the following melodies in the other clef without changing the pitch.

Debussy, Prelude Voiles

a)

Sibelius, Symphony No.3, 3rd Movement

b)

Mozart, Piano Concerto K270

c)

Glinka, Souvenir of a Night in Madrid

d)

Prokofiev, Flute Sonata in D Op.94

e)

Time Signatures

A time signature has two numbers.

4   This shows the *kind of time*, i.e. the number of beats in a bar.
2   This shows the *kind of beat* used.

By looking at the top figure, the kind of time can be described as:

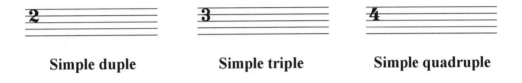

      Simple duple   **Simple triple**   **Simple quadruple**

The bottom figure represents:

      Crotchet beats   **Minim beats**   **Quaver beats**

Thus, the time signature $\frac{3}{2}$ means *simple triple*, *minim beats* or 3 minim beats in a bar.

The time signature $\frac{2}{2}$ can also be written as ¢ (also known as **alla breve**).

(In grade 1, the time signatures learnt are $\frac{2}{4}$, $\frac{3}{4}$ and $\frac{4}{4}$)

(In grade 2, the new time signatures to be included are $\frac{2}{2}$, $\frac{3}{2}$, $\frac{4}{2}$ and $\frac{3}{8}$)

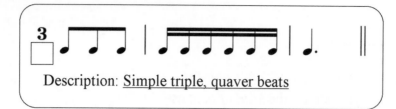
Description: Simple triple, quaver beats

a) Description:_____

b) Description:_____

c) Description:_____

d) Description:_____

e) Description:_____

f) Description:_____

6

Britten, Simple Symphony (4th movt)

a)

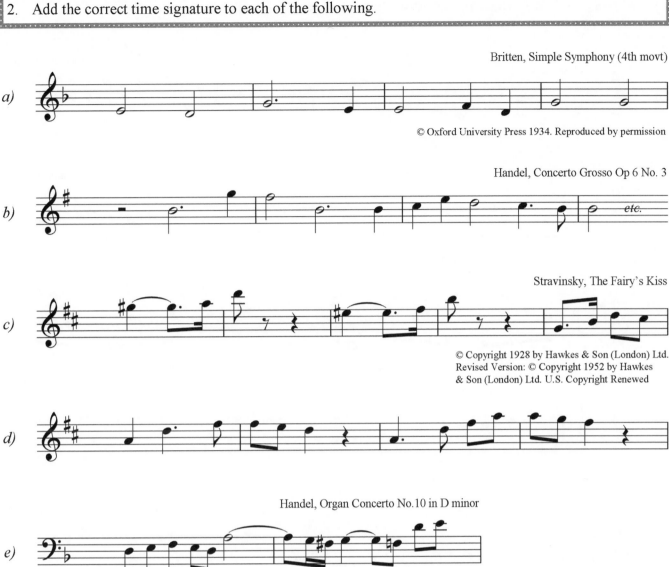

Handel, Concerto Grosso Op 6 No. 3

b)

Stravinsky, The Fairy's Kiss

c)

d)

Handel, Organ Concerto No.10 in D minor

e)

Scarlatti, The Good Humored Ladies Ballet Suite

f)

Holst, Hymn Tune

g)

Schumann, Papillons Op. 2 No.11

h)

3. Add the missing bar-lines to each of the following. Start on the first beat of the bar.

Mozart, Trio in C

a)

Schumann, Symphony No.2

b)

Scarlatti, Sonata Largo 463

c)

Handel, Water Music (10th movt.)

d)

Shostakovich, Symphony No.6 Op.53

e)

Bach, Brandenberg Concerto No.2

f)

Vaughan Williams, Hymn Tune

g)

Haydn, Symphony No.92

h)

4. Rewrite the following rhythms using notes of half the time value. Remember to insert the new time signature.

a)

b)

c)

5. Rewrite the following rhythms using notes of double the time value. Remember to insert the new time signature.

a)

b)

c)

9

Triplets

A beat that can be divided into two equal parts can also be divided into three. This is called a *triplet* and is written with a ⌞—3—⌟ or ‿3 :

Other equivalents of the triplets include:

1. Write the time signature for each of the one-bar rhythms.

a)

b)

c)

d)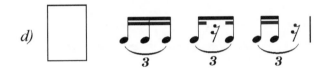

e)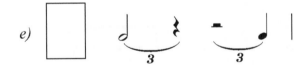

f)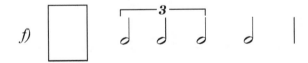

g)

h)

i)

j)

k)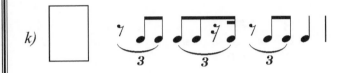

l)

m)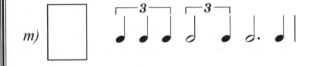

n)

o)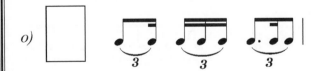

p)

11

2. Add bar-lines to the following rhythms and then write the beats of each bar in their correct places below the notes. An example has been shown.

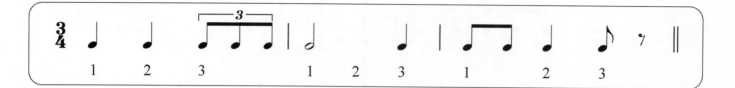

a)

b)

c)

d)

e)

f)

g)

12

The Scales and Key Signatures of A, B♭ and E♭ Major

A major scale consists of eight notes (in an octave) built on tones and semitones. For example:

C major

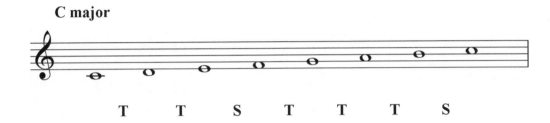

T   T   S   T   T   T   S

T - Tones
S - Semitones

Here are more major scales:

A major

B♭ major

E♭ major

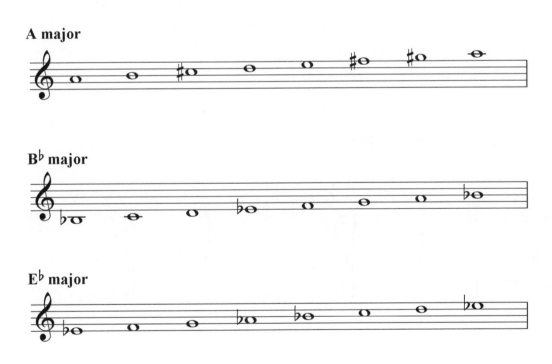

All the major scales in grades 1 and 2 can be presented as:

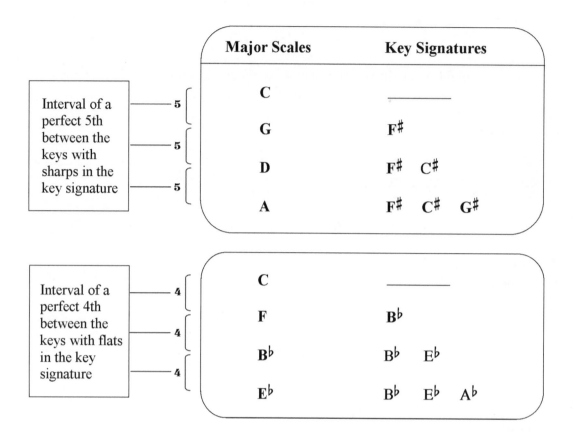

	Major Scales	Key Signatures
	C	————
	G	F♯
	D	F♯ C♯
	A	F♯ C♯ G♯

Interval of a perfect 5th between the keys with sharps in the key signature — 5, 5, 5

	Major Scales	Key Signatures
	C	————
	F	B♭
	B♭	B♭ E♭
	E♭	B♭ E♭ A♭

Interval of a perfect 4th between the keys with flats in the key signature — 4, 4, 4

The tonic triads and key signatures of the new major scales are:

A major

B♭ major

E♭ major

1. Write the major scales of the following keys using the correct key signature. Slur the semitones. An example has been shown.

B♭ major

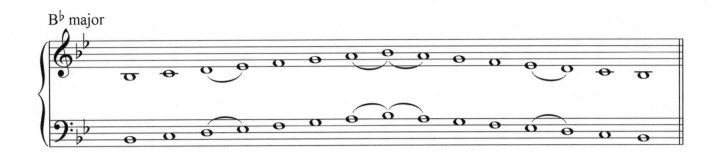

a) E♭ major

b) A major

c) D major

d) G major

B♭ major

a) G major

b) D major

c) E♭ major

d) A major

16

3. Write the tonic triads of the following keys using the correct key signature.

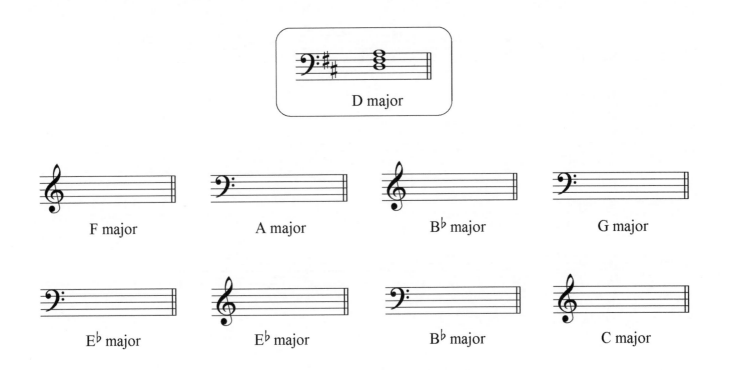

D major

F major   A major   B♭ major   G major

E♭ major   E♭ major   B♭ major   C major

4. Write the tonic triads of the following keys using any necessary accidentals.

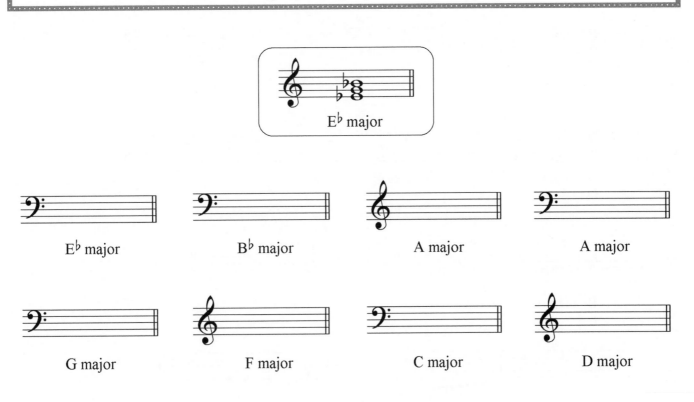

E♭ major

E♭ major   B♭ major   A major   A major

G major   F major   C major   D major

5. Add the correct clef and any necessary accidentals to form the major scales of the keys named.

a)

B♭ major

b)

A major

c)

D major

d)

A major

e)

E♭ major

f)

G major

g)

B♭ major

h)

E♭ major

The Scales and Key Signatures of A, D and E Minor

There are two types of minor scales:

(i) **The harmonic minor** (*The ascending form is* **the same** *as the descending form.*)

A minor

(ii) **The melodic minor** (*The ascending and descending forms are* **different**.)

A minor

The semitones have been marked with a *slur*.

The other minor scales are:

E harmonic minor

E melodic minor

D harmonic minor

D melodic minor

Each minor scale is said to be **related** to a major key and vice versa. (Notice that the major key has the same notes as the descending form of the relative minor key, but they start and end on different key notes.)

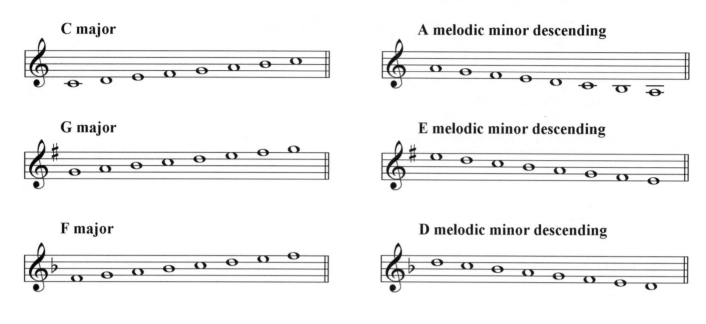

The relationship may be summarised as follows:

Major Key	Key Signature	Relative Minor	Harmonic Form (raised 7th note)	Melodic Form			
				ascending: raised 6th & 7th notes		descending: lower 6th & 7th notes	
C	——	A	G♯	F♯	G♯ ,	G♮	F♮
G	F♯	E	D♯	C♯	D♯ ,	D♮	C♮
F	B♭	D	C♯	B♮	C♯ ,	C♮	B♭

1. Using the correct key signature, write the following minor scales in crotchets. You may choose either the melodic or harmonic form. Slur the semitones. An example has been shown.

E minor (harmonic form)

20

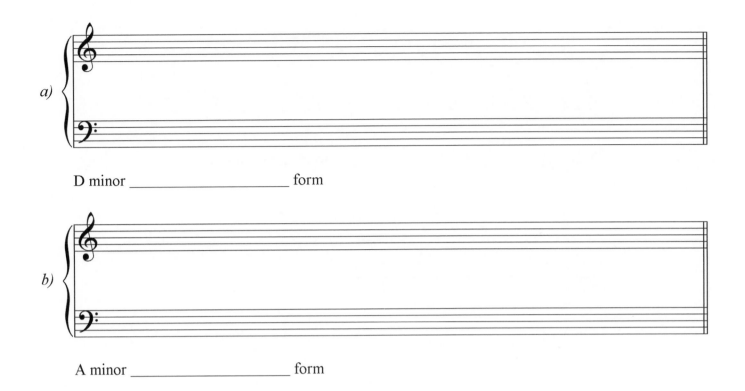

a)

D minor _____ form

b)

A minor _____ form

---

2. Using the given rhythms, write the minor scales as named below. Do not use a key signature, but add any necessary accidentals. Indicate which form of the scale you have used.

A minor (<u>melodic</u> form, ascending)

a)

E minor (_____ form, descending)

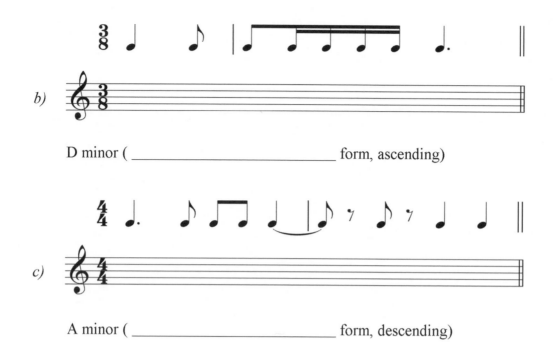

b) D minor (_____ form, ascending)

c) A minor (_____ form, descending)

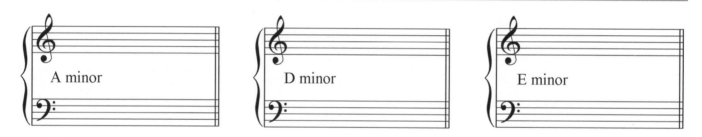

3. Write the tonic triads of the minor keys named. Use the appropriate key signature.

A minor

D minor

E minor

4. The given note is the key-note of a minor key. Write the tonic triad after it. Do not use a key signature. Remember to name the key.

Key :   D minor

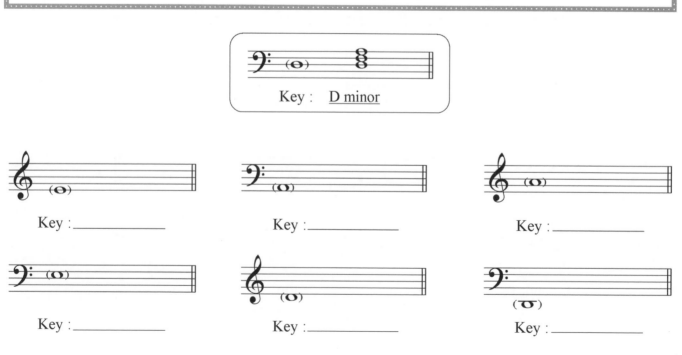

Key :_____

Key :_____

Key :_____

Key :_____

Key :_____

Key :_____

Supplementary Exercises

1. Add the correct clefs and any necessary accidentals to form the major scales named.

a)

Eᵇ major

b)

F major

c)

A major

2. Name the key of each of the following. Then write them out again, using the correct key signature but leaving out the unnecessary accidentals. An example has been shown.

Beethoven, Sonata No 3 for cello & piano

Key: <u>A major</u>

Berlioz, Fantastique Symphony (4th movt)

a)

Key: _____

b) Bach, English Suite No.6 Courante

Key :_____

c) Britten, Simple Symphony

Key :_____

© Oxford University Press 1934. Reproduced by permission

d) Chopin, Nocturne Op.72 No.1

Key :_____

e) Chopin, Sonata in G minor for Cello & Piano

Key :_____

f) Haydn, Symphony in E♭ No.99

Key :_____

Elgar, Sonata in E minor for Violin & Piano

g)

Key :_____

Haydn, Drum Roll Symphony (3rd movt)

h)

Key :_____

3. Name the keys of the tonic triads below.

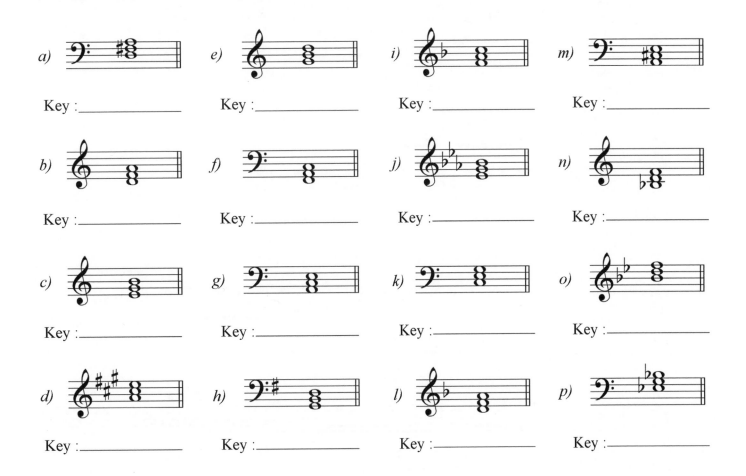

a)

Key :_____

e)

Key :_____

i)

Key :_____

m)

Key :_____

b)

Key :_____

f)

Key :_____

j)

Key :_____

n)

Key :_____

c)

Key :_____

g)

Key :_____

k)

Key :_____

o)

Key :_____

d)

Key :_____

h)

Key :_____

l)

Key :_____

p)

Key :_____

Degree of the Scale and Intervals

In a scale, the key-note is called the first degree of the scale, followed by the 2nd, 3rd, 4th, 5th and so on:

Degree of scale: 1st   2nd   3rd   4th   5th   6th   7th   8ve

> 1. Write the number of the degree of the scale (2nd, 3rd, 4th etc.) under each of the notes marked * .
> The first two notes have been shown.

Beethoven, Concerto No.4

a)

G major   1st   7th   ___   ___   ___   ___

Brahms, Concerto in D (2nd movt)

b)

F major   ___   ___   ___   ___   ___   ___

c)

D minor   ___   ___   ___   ___

d)

A major   ___   ___   ___   ___   ___

e)

E minor   ___   ___   ___   ___   ___   ___

The distance in pitch between two notes is called an **interval**. The size of an interval is measured by the number of degrees of the scale between the two notes:

4th   5th

If the two notes are played together, it is a **harmonic** interval.
If the two notes are played one after another, it is a **melodic** interval.

Here are the intervals built from the key-note of D minor:

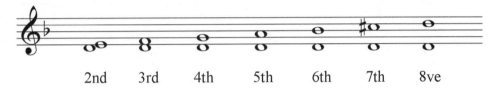

2nd   3rd   4th   5th   6th   7th   8ve

2.   Give the number of the following melodic intervals.

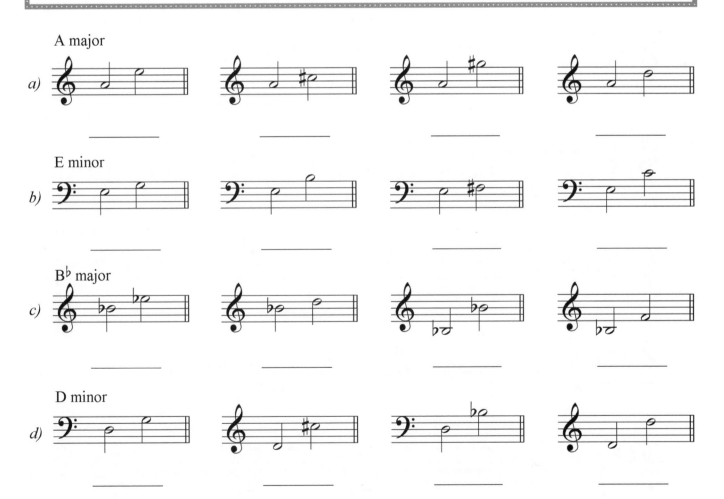

3. Give the number of each of the following harmonic intervals. The lower note is the key-note.

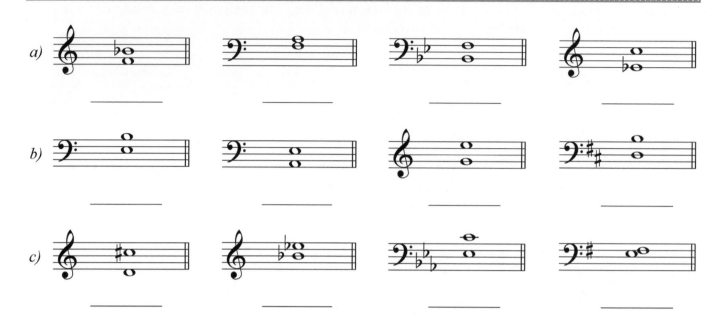

a)

_____   _____   _____   _____

b)

_____   _____   _____   _____

c)

_____   _____   _____   _____

4. Give the number of each of the following harmonic intervals marked ⌐‾‾‾¬ . Each interval is to be described from the lower of the two notes.

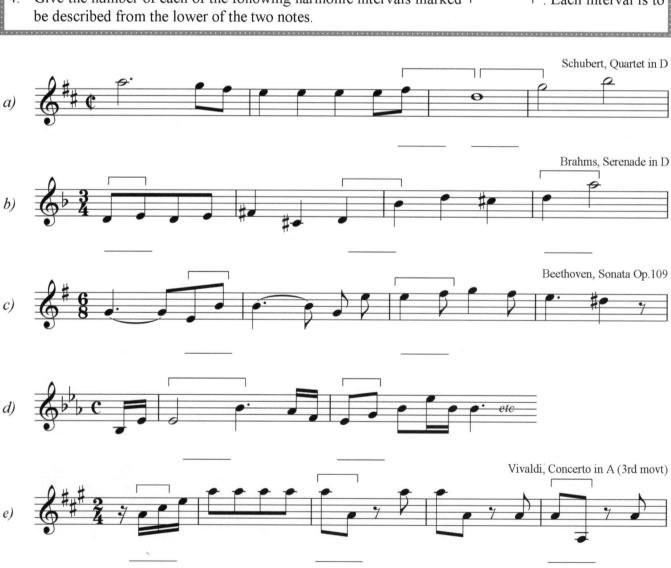

Schubert, Quartet in D

a)

_____   _____

Brahms, Serenade in D

b)

_____   _____

Beethoven, Sonata Op.109

c)

_____   _____

d)

_____   _____

Vivaldi, Concerto in A (3rd movt)

e)

_____   _____

28

Grouping of Notes and Beaming

2/2, 3/2 and 4/2 Time

Use a semibreve instead of 2 tied minims within a bar:

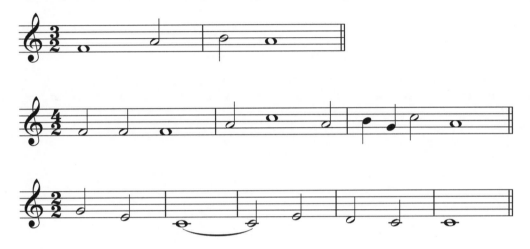

Beam quavers by minim beats:

Beam semiquavers by crotchet beats:

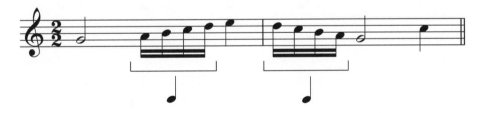

3/8 Time

In 3/8 time, beam all quavers and semiquavers into a complete bar:

1. Rewrite the following rhythms, grouping the notes correctly without changing the effect.

a)

b)

c)

d)

e)

30

Beaming

Notes that are beamed together must have all the stems in one direction, either up or down:

For example:  and

For:  it should be beamed

since, of the two notes,  is further away from the center of the stave.

2. Rewrite the passages below by beaming the notes correctly.

a)

b)

c)

Grouping of Rests

A bar rest in $\frac{2}{4}$, $\frac{3}{4}$, $\frac{4}{4}$, $\frac{2}{2}$, $\frac{3}{2}$ and $\frac{3}{8}$ is written as ▬ .

In quadruple time, the rest or rests are grouped thus:

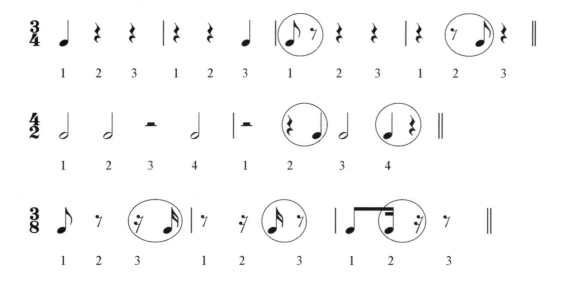

Do not group:

In other time signatures, group the rest(s) according to each beat.

Shorter rests are grouped in half beats.

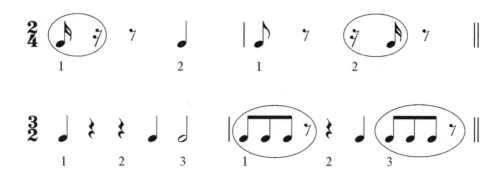

Do not write more rests than necessary.

---

1. Rewrite the passages below to show the correct grouping for the rests.

33

e)

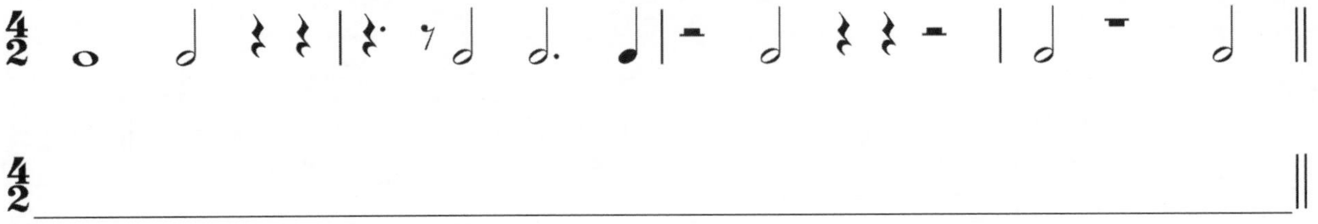

f)

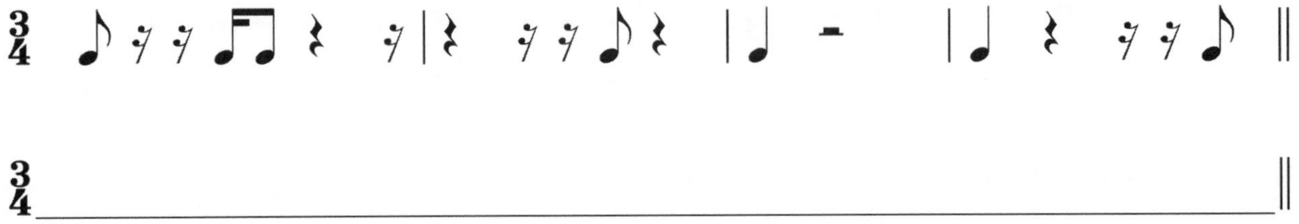

g)

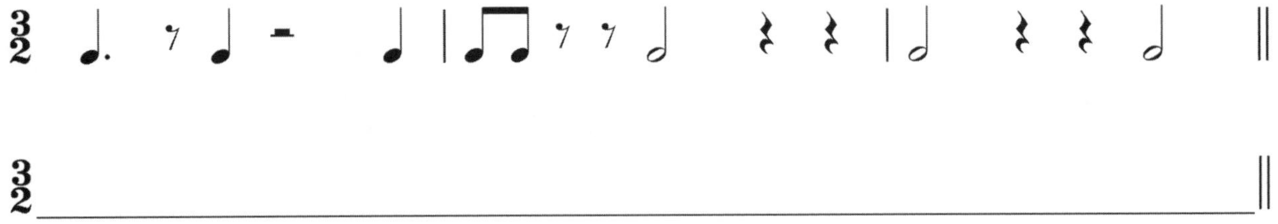

h)

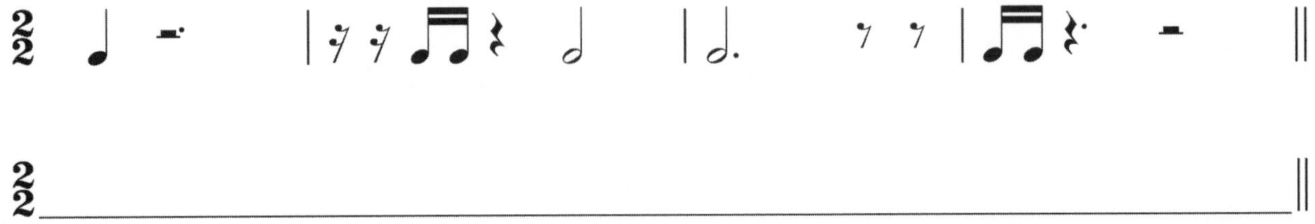

i)

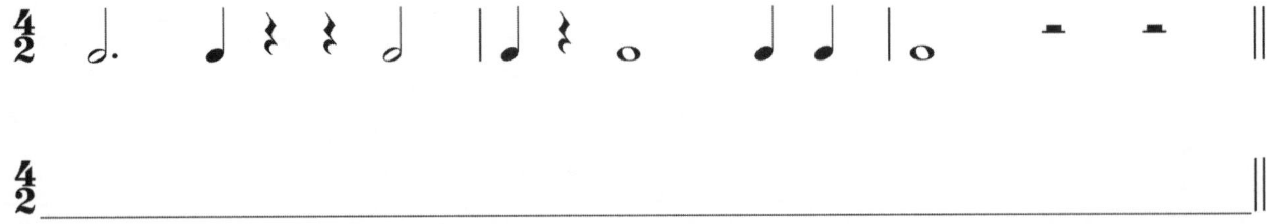

j)

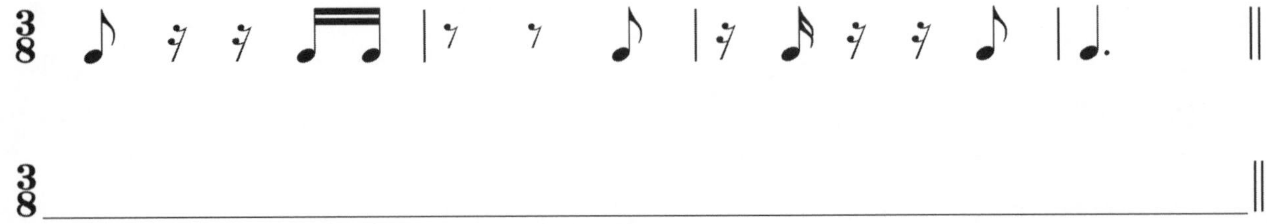

2. Rewrite the melodies below correcting any mistakes in the grouping of notes and rests. An example has been shown.

Elgar, Enigma Variations

a)

Handel, Water Music

b)

Schumann, Symphony No.3

c)

Mahler, Resurrection Symphony (1st movt)

d)

Grieg, Norwegian Melody

e)

Composing Simple Four-bar Rhythms

Most musical phrases show a sense of structure and design in the use of rhythm:

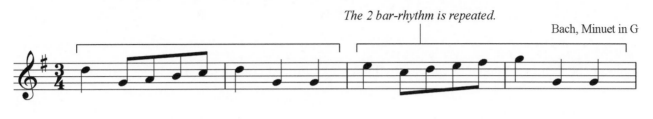

The 2 bar-rhythm is repeated.

Bach, Minuet in G

Repetition is one of the most commonly used features:

ABAB

A   **B**   **A**   **B**

ABAC

A   **B**   **A**   **C**

ABCB

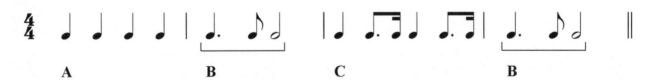

A   **B**   **C**   **B**

ABBC

A   **B**   **B**   **C**

AAAB

A   **A**   **A**   **B**

ABBB

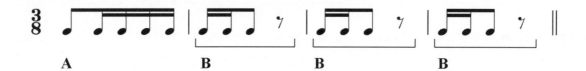

A   B   B   B

Some musical phrases may contain no rhythmic repetition of complete bars.

Avoid using too many different rhythms in every bar. It is unmusical.

Write rhythms that show unity and regularity in the patterns.

A musical phrase usually ends effectively with a long note or a rest.

---

1. In each of the following, mark with a ⌐‾‾‾¬ to show the bars with the same rhythm. Identify the rhythmic pattern as shown in the example.

Holst, Hymn Tune 'Craham'

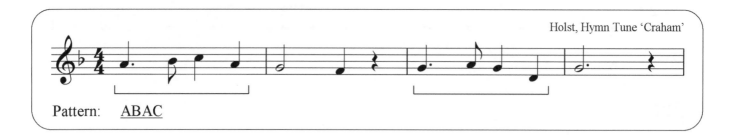

Pattern: <u>ABAC</u>

Mozart, Divertimento in F K138

a)

Pattern:_____

b) Grieg, Concerto Op.16

Pattern:_____

c) Mozart, Sonata in C K545

Pattern:_____

d) Rachmaninoff, Concerto No.2 in C minor

Pattern:_____

e) Schubert, Symphony No.4 (4th movt)

Pattern:_____

f) Schubert, Concertante in F

Pattern:_____

g) Beethoven, Concerto in D, Op.61

Pattern:_____

h) Debussy, Golliwog's Cake-Walk

Pattern:_____

2. Create 4-bar rhythms for each of the following opening bars. Use the rhythmic design as suggested.

a) Use **ABAB**

i)

ii)

iii)

iv)

b) Use **ABAC**

i)

ii)

iii)

iv)

c) Use **ABCB**

i)

ii)

iii)

iv)

d) Use **ABCD (no repetition)**

i)

ii)

iii)

iv)

3. Write 4-bar rhythms for each of the following openings. You may use any type of rhythmic design you wish.

a)

b)

c)

d)

e)

f)

g)

h)

i)

Musical Terms and Signs

Here are all the terms and signs you should know, including those in the Grade 1 syllabus.

Musical Terms

a	at, to, by, for, in, in the style of
accelerando (or *accel.*)	gradually getting quicker
adagio	slow
al, alla	to the, in the manner of
alla marcia	in the style of a march
allargando	broadening, getting a little slower and probably a little louder
allegretto	fairly quick (but not as quick as *allegro*)
allegro	quick, lively
allegro assai	very quick
allegro moderato	moderately quick
andante	at a medium ('walking') speed
andantino	rather slow (slightly faster or slower than andante)
assai	very
cantabile	in a singing style
con, col	with
con moto	with movement
crescendo, cresc.	gradually getting louder
Da capo, D.C	repeat from the beginning
Dal segno, D.S.	repeat from the sign 𝄋
decrescendo, decresc.	gradually getting softer
diminuendo, dim.	gradually getting softer
dolce	sweet, soft
e, ed	and
espressivo, espress., espr.	expressive
fine	the end
forte, **𝒇**	loud
fortissimo, **𝒇𝒇**	very loud
fortepiano, **𝒇𝒑**	loud, then immediately soft
giocoso	playful, merry
grave	very slow, solemn
grazioso	graceful
larghetto	rather slow (but not as slow as largo)
largo	slow, stately

legato	smooth
lento	slow
ma	but
maestoso	majestic
meno	less
meno mosso	less movement
mezzo	half
mezzo forte, **mf**	moderately loud
mezzo piano, **mp**	moderately soft
moderato	moderately
molto	very, much
mosso, moto	movement
non	not
non troppo	not too much
piano, **p**	soft
pianissimo, **pp**	very soft
più	more
poco	a little
presto	very fast
rallentando, rall.	getting gradually slower
ritardando, ritard., rit.	getting gradually slower
ritenuto, riten., rit.	held back
senza	without
sforzando, sforzato, **sf**, **sfz**	forced, accented
simile, or *sim.*	in the same way
sostenuto	sustained
tenuto	held
troppo	too much
vivace, vivo	lively, quick

Musical Signs

Accent the notes
∧ (over) and ∨ (under) mean the same, or even stronger accents.

Slightly detached notes.

Very short and strongly accented notes.

With slightly held accents and slightly separated.

44

1. Explain the following terms.

1. On Speed *(Tempo)*

allargando : _____

andantino : _____

a tempo : _____

larghetto : _____

largo : _____

mosso, moto : _____

meno mosso : _____

con moto : _____

piu mosso : _____

presto : _____

vivace, vivo : _____

rall. : _____

lento : _____

moderato : _____

2. On Dynamics

fp (fortepiano) : _____

sf, sfz (sforzando, sforzato) : _____

mf : _____

cresc. : _____

diminuendo : _____

ff : _____

45

3. On Performance Style

dolce : _____

espressivo : _____

giocoso : _____

grave : _____

grazioso : _____

maestoso : _____

sostenuto : _____

tenuto : _____

simile : _____

4. Others:

These words can only be used with another term:

A : _____

　　　　　　　　　　a tempo : _____

Al, alla : _____

　　　　　　　　　　alla marcia : _____

Assai : _____

　　　　　　　　　　allegro assai : _____

Con, : _____

　　　　　　　　　　con spirito : _____

E, ed : _____

　　　　　　　　　　p e dolce : _____

Ma : _____

                              ma non troppo: _____

Meno : _____

                              meno mosso: _____

Non : _____

                              non troppo: _____

Piu : _____

                              piu mosso: _____

Senza : _____

                              senza rit: _____

---

2.   Explain the following signs:

                                        _____

                                          _____

                                          _____

                                          _____

                                          _____

                                          _____

General Exercises

1. Look at this melody and then answer the questions that follow.

Schumann, Erinnerung
1
2
3
4
5
p
6
7
8
9
10

a) In what key does this melody begin? ______________________________

b) Which degree of the scale is the first note? ______________________________

c) Name the four types of note values used in the extract. (i.e. quaver, crotchet etc.)

i) ______________________ *iii)* ______________________

ii) ______________________ *iv)* ______________________

d) Give the number of the interval marked └──┘ in bars 7 and 10.

i) (bar 7) ________________ *ii)* (bar 10) ________________

e) Circle any one of the following which did not occur in the music.

phrase   tie   slur   dotted note

f) The melody is to be played sweetly. Choose one of the following words and write it under the stave in bar 1.

legato   spirito   maestoso   dolce   espressivo

g) Circle a *rather slow* tempo which is suitable for the melody.

allegro   largo   andantino   presto   vivo

h) Write the key signature in the bass clef

i) Copy the music from the beginning to the first note of bar 4 in notes of double the value. Use the new time signature.

2. Look at the melody and then answer the questions that follow.

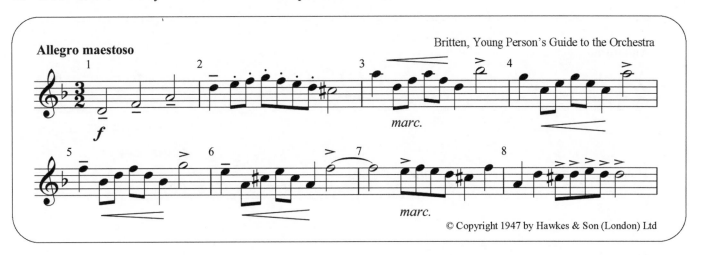

Allegro maestoso

a) In what key does the melody begin? _____

b) Name another key which has the same key signature. _____

c) Describe the time signature. (i.e. duple, triple etc.) _____

d) Which bar contains only the notes of the tonic triad?   Bar_____

e) Copy the rhythm that has been repeated four times in the passage?

$\frac{3}{2}$ _____

f) Circle two notes which form   i) a semitone.   ii) an interval of a 6th.

g) Name the only tied note. _____

h) What is the Italian word for the sign ⟨cresc. sign⟩ ? _____

   What does it mean? _____

i) Give the meaning of each of the following words and signs:

   allegro   _____

   maestoso   _____

   𝅗𝅥 (bar 1)   _____

   𝆗𝅗𝅥 (bar 3)   _____

   𝅘𝅥. (bar 2)   _____

   marc. (bars 3 and 7)   _____

49

3. Look at the melody and then answer the questions that follow.

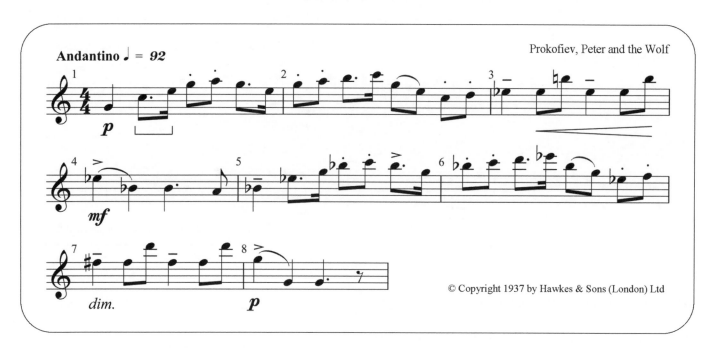

a) Explain Andantino ♩ = 92 . _____

b) Name the interval marked with a ⌞_____⌟ (bar 1). _____

c) Circle two notes which form a semitone.

d) How many notes are written using ledger lines? _____

e) Where is the rhythm of bars 1 to 3 repeated? Bars _____ to _____

f) Give the meaning of the following

     p   (bar 1) _____

     ◁   (bar 3) _____

     mf   (bar 4) _____

     dim .   (bar 7) _____

g) What is another Italian word which means the same as *dim.*? _____

h) Two notes in bars 5 and 6 have accidentals. These notes are _____ and _____ .

i) How many times in the extract does the rhythm ♩. ♩ occur? _____ times

j) After each of these notes, write a rest of the same value.

Specimen Test

Duration 1½ hours

Answer ALL questions.

Total Marks
100

1. Rewrite the following with the notes correctly grouped (beamed). Add rests to the last bar so as to make it complete.

10

2. Write a four-bar rhythm using this opening.

10

3. Add the missing figure to the time signature in each of the following.

10

4. Give the letter name of each of the notes, including the sharp, flat or natural sign where necessary.

___   ___   ___   ___   ___

___   ___   ___   ___   ___

5(a) Write the tonic triad of each of the keys named. Do not use a key signature but add any necessary accidentals.

E♭ major   B♭ major   D minor

5(b) Name the key of each of the following tonic triads:

   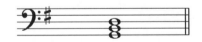

Key: _____   Key: _____

6. Using the given rhythm, write the scales named below. Use the correct key signature. | 10 |

E♭ major, descending

E minor, ascending

Which form of the minor scale have you used?_____

7. Give the number of the following harmonic intervals (2nd, 3rd and 4th etc.): | 10 |

The key is G major.

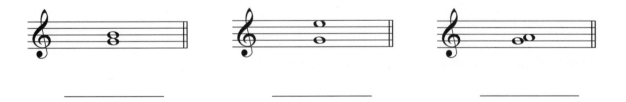

_____   _____   _____

_____   _____

8. Look at this melody, and then answer the questions below:

(a) (i)   What is the key of the melody?_____

    (ii) Circle three notes within a bar which form the tonic triad.

    (iii) The time signature may also be written as _____

    (iv) Put a ⌐___⌐ under two notes which form the interval of an octave.

    (v)   The speed of this melody is ♩ = 84 . Circle a word which suits the speed of this march.

          andante   lento   allegro   allegretto   presto

```
10
```

(b) (i)   Give the time names of these rests. (e.g. crotchet, quaver etc.)

          ⸜ _____   ⸜ _____   𝄽 _____

    (ii) What is the Italian word which is the opposite of *cresc.*? _____

    (iii) Rewrite the last bar using the bass clef

```
10
```

_____
_____
_____
_____
_____

(c)   Mark with a ⌒ , the bar(s) which repeat(s) the rhythm of bar 1.

4

(d)   Explain these signs:

$\hat{\rho}$

(bar 5) _____

$\downarrow$
sf

(bar 8) _____

(bar 6) _____

(bar 1) _____

6